Grandpa, Gra[illegible]

by Joy Cowley

Grandpa, Grandpa,
come with me.

Let's go fishing
in the sea.

What will we fish for?
What will we get?

One pot of mussels
for our tea.

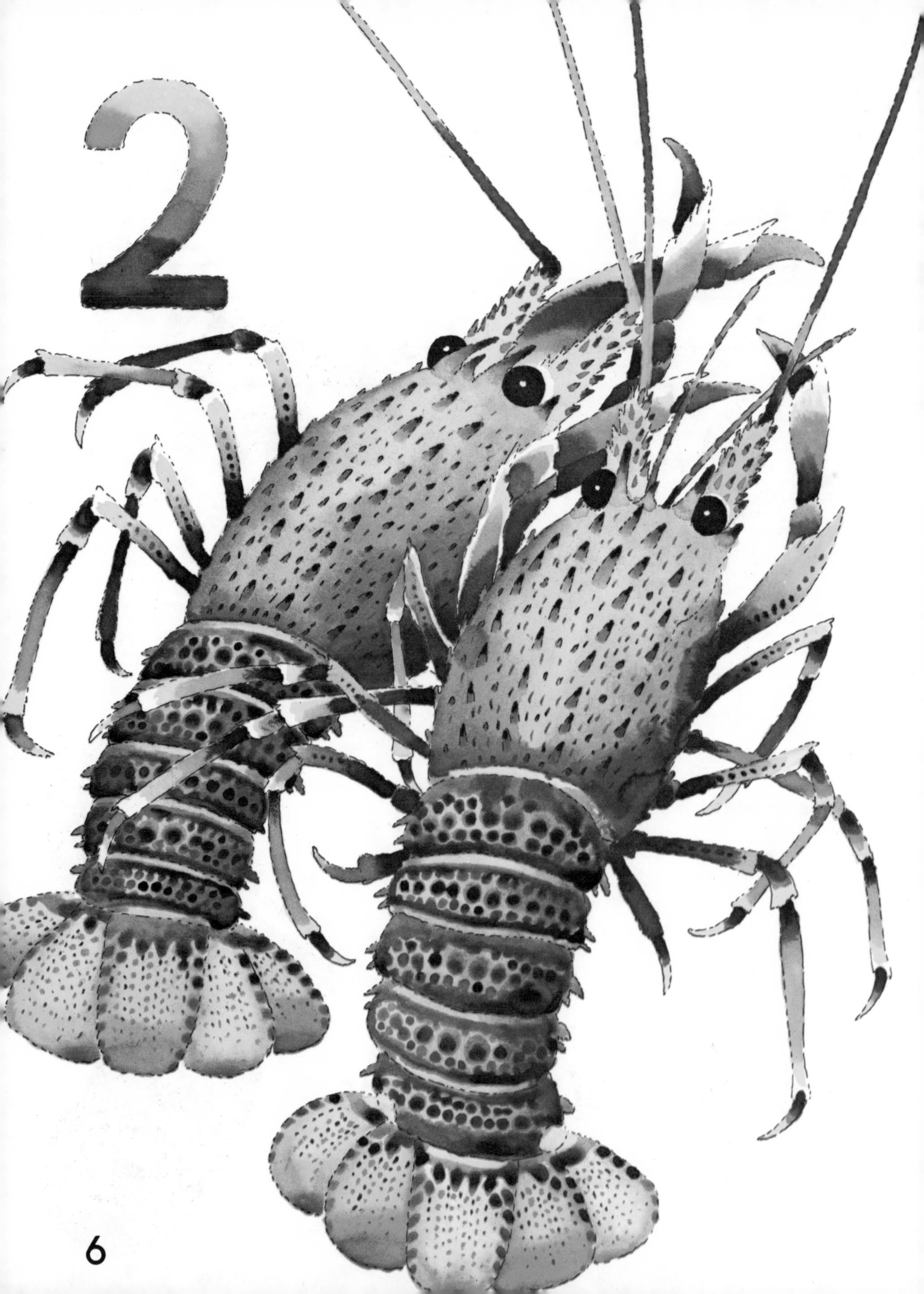
2

Grandpa, Grandpa,
come with me.
Let's go fishing
in the sea.

What will we fish for?
What will we get?

Two big crayfish
for our tea.

Grandpa, Grandpa,
come with me.
Let's go fishing
in the sea.

What will we fish for?
What will we get?

3

Three fat snapper
for our tea.

Grandpa said
he'd come with me,
and we went fishing
in the sea.

What did we fish for?
What did we get?

1
2
3

One pot of mussels,
two big crayfish,
three fat snapper
for our tea.

What else did we get?
We got wet!